The Legend

of

Hanukkah Harry

by

Irv Korman

Illustrations by

Chloe Corbett

Twin Sisters Press

ISBN 978-1-937979-31-7

http://www.twinsisterspress.com/

This book is dedicated to:

Courtney Kreiger

and

Sharona Hoffman

Best always,

Jw Korman

Special "Thank You"

This book would not be possible without the help and advice from the following:

Rabbi Robert Feinberg

Rabbi Norman "Nachum" Lipson

Rabbi David M. Horowitz

Rabbi Joshua Brown

Cantor Philip L. Sherman

Tony Acree

James O. Barnes

Dominic Frisina

Suzanne Houston

David Koch

Francine Korman

Judy Lasher

Allison and Wayne Marks

Carolyn Narotsky

Bill O'Connor

Barbara Renstrom

Arlene Rossen

A very special "thank you" to Julie Korman for research and help.

A very, very special, special "thank you" to Melanie Korman for technical assistance and "always being there."

PROLOGUE

I was born in Akron, Ohio, USA, on June 29, 1945, at 11:28 AM, EST.

Nazi Germany had surrendered one month before in May, 1945. Japan would surrender a few months later, in September, 1945, to officially end World War II.

The Midwestern city of Cleveland, Ohio, rests on the southern shoreline of Lake Erie, one of the five Great Lakes. Akron is located just thirty miles south of Cleveland.

Akron, Ohio, was once the world headquarters for several tire and rubber companies. Among them were Goodyear, Goodrich, Firestone, and General, thus giving the city of Akron the international title of "The Rubber Capitol of the World."

Akron, Ohio, was often referred to as "The Capital of West Virginia." This was due to the migration north of West Virginians up State Route 77, to Akron, to find employment in the Akron tire and rubber factories. In fact, for many West Virginians, "The Three R's" meant "**R**eadin', **R**itin", and **R**oute 77."

I recently learned of Akron, Ohio's importance, during World War II. Because of its many tire and rubber factories, Akron was ranked approximately #5 on the "hit list" of United States cities to be destroyed by our enemies.

From 1950 to 1960, I attended Schumacher and Maple Valley elementary schools (kindergarten through sixth grade), then to Simon Perkins Junior High School (grades 7 through 9) in the Akron Public School system. Then it was grades 10 through 12 at John R. Buchtel High School, graduating with my high school diploma in June of 1963.

The population of Akron, Ohio, from the mid-1950's, to the early 1960's reached almost 300,000 inhabitants. A fraction of that statistic included approximately 5,500 of the Jewish faith (that included me).

The Jewish population of Akron, Ohio, though statistically small and a distinct minority, was large enough to support three synagogues: one Orthodox, one Conservative, and one Reform. This unique population supported an active Jewish Center for educational and social activities, as well as many philanthropic organizations.

Every Tuesday evening at The Akron Jewish Center was "Young Adult Night," set aside for Jewish teenagers. Several boys clubs and girls clubs met for about two hours, in upstairs classrooms. Most of the boys clubs were local chapters of AZA (Aleph Zadik Aleph), while the girls clubs were locals of BBG (B'nai B'rith Girls). After their club meetings the teens would filter down to the lower-level AJC social lounge to listen to the latest Rock 'n' Roll, 45RPM records, in order to dance and socialize.

It was into this middle class atmosphere, aside from Sunday school and Hebrew School, that we of the Jewish faith, functioned in the mostly Christian, Akron, Ohio, community.

I vividly remember properly folding my hands and reciting The Lord's Prayer every morning in my elementary public school classroom before pledging allegiance to the United States flag. I recall dying colorful Easter eggs in my elementary public school classroom for an Easter basket I did not have. I made Christmas decorations, for a Christmas tree I also did not have.

In the spring, the Jewish holiday of Passover usually coincided with the Christian holiday of Easter. Passover historically commemorates the Jewish nation leaving Egypt as slaves to begin their epic 40-year journey through the desert to "The Promised Land" of Israel, led by Moses. It was an ongoing joke to tell my non-Jewish friends that Passover to us Jews meant the Easter Bunny would "*pass over*" our Jewish home and *not* leave an Easter basket of dyed Easter eggs, jelly beans, and chocolate Easter bunnies.

Another holiday coincidence usually occurred in December. While Christians celebrated Christmas, we, in the Jewish community, celebrated Hanukkah. Everyone knew the story of Christmas and the birth of Christ, but many non-Jews, however, did not know the story of Hanukkah. It is the eight-day celebration commemorating the victory of the Jewish Maccabees over the Greek-Syrians. Hanukkah also commemorates the re-dedication of the Second Temple in 164 BCE. The victorious Maccabees wanted to re-purify the desecrated Temple by burning ritual oil for eight nights. Only a small amount of oil was found in a bottle, enough for only one night. Miraculously, the oil lasted eight nights!

In December, just before Christmas vacation, each Akron Public School put on its annual Christmas program. The first performance was in front of the entire school during school time. The second performance was at night for parents, friends, and relatives. The school choir and orchestra consisted of several Jewish participants who performed in the Christmas program. The eight-day Jewish celebration of Hanukkah was never acknowledged. Even into the 1980's, when my two daughters attended public elementary school, little had changed with the exception of somewhere near the end of the "Winter Holiday Program" a rendition of "I Had A Little Dreidel" would be sung, almost as an obvious after-thought.

I recall my Christian friends telling me about Santa Claus delivering toys to all the "good" girls and boys. I never got toys from Santa Claus. Did that mean I was "bad?" In actuality, some of my Jewish friends and I *did go* to the downtown department stores to visit Santa Claus, sit on his lap, and tell the man in the red suit what we wanted for Christmas. We did it to get a free toy just for visiting him.

"Santa" couldn't tell who was Jewish or Christian. I often wondered if the man in the red Santa Claus suit was even Christian himself!

(Author's Note: I, myself, have been portraying Santa Claus for over 40 years during the Christmas season!)

Who, back in the 1950's, did I have to counter Santa Claus?

Over the years I heard a few vague references made about a character named "Hanukkah Harry." Who was he and where did he come from? No information was available with the exception of a few "Saturday Night Live" comedy sketches on NBC-TV in the late 1980's. Comic John Lovitz portrayed "Hanukkah Harry" in a few humorous skits.

For my own very personal reasons, I decided to create my *own* legend of "Hanukkah Harry."

You may ask: Are there any similarities between "Hanukkah Harry" and Santa Claus? Indeed!

Does "Hanukkah Harry" deliver toys to good Jewish girls and boys? You bet!

You may also ask, "Why 'Hanukkah Harry'?" Is it Santa Claus "envy"? In truth, I think so.

But my answer as to *why* create a legend of "Hanukkah Harry" is simple and personal for me.

Imagine if a "Hanukkah Harry" book was available in the 1950's when I was in elementary school when my Christian classmates taunted me with, "You don't get any toys from Santa Claus because you aren't Christian! Ha! Ha! Ha!"

Back then, I would have said: "You can keep your Santa Claus and only *one* day of Christmas for your good Christian girls and boys! I have my very own 'Hanukkah Harry' for good *Jewish* girls and boys. Besides, we get EIGHT nights of presents: not just one!"

The aforementioned situation may have helped at least one little confused Jewish boy, better cope, in the mid 1950's, in mostly-Christian, Akron, Ohio.

FORWARD

When I was a teenager I occasionally attended Friday evening Shabbat services at Beth-El Congregation, Akron, Ohio's conservative synagogue. I could also walk to Beth-El for Saturday morning Shabbat services. Arriving at my synagogue, I would notice one old man in particular. He always sat in the last row of the main sanctuary and prayed by himself. I never knew how he got there or how he got home. I didn't even know where he lived or what he did. What amazed me most of all was the fact that he *never, **ever*** used a prayer book! He recited all the prayers, in Hebrew, *by heart*!

(Author's Note: Most people thought I went to Saturday morning Shabbat services because I was religious. That was not my main motivation. Mr. Arthur Tirsun, Beth-El's young adult education director, would give a large candy bar to any young adult who attended that Shabbat morning's service. I don't know what Mr. Tirsun called it back in the 1950's, but today I call it "incentive.")

The old man I would see at Beth-El every Shabbat, always wore a black suit, white shirt, and thin black tie. He kept to himself. I couldn't tell how tall he was because he was always bent over at the waist whenever he stood up to pray. I would hear some kind of "foreign" accent when he spoke to other adults. Some said he came from "the old country," which usually meant Eastern Europe. He also wore a different style "yarmulke," or skull cap on his head. It was black and shiny, but not like the ones in the wooden box at the entrance to the main sanctuary. His skull cap was tall and foreign-looking. Like the old man himself, the skull cap was different and mysterious-looking to me.

People called the old man "Nachum."

I often thought Nachum might have been a Holocaust survivor. Perhaps he made a secret pact with God that if he survived the Holocaust he would go to Shabbat services every week to repay the "debt" to God for sparing his life.

My teenage friends and I thought the old man came to Shabbat services every week just because of the "Kiddush," the desserts served after prayer services. The best ones were right after Saturday morning Bar Mitzvahs. That's when they served herring and schnapps besides the usual sponge cake and hot tea and coffee!

One Shabbat Saturday morning I finally got up enough nerve (due to a dare from my friends) to wish old Nachum, "Happy Hanukkah." I routinely wished him a happy holiday, especially on Sukkot, Rosh Hashanah, Yom Kippur, Simchat Torah, etc. But Nachum never returned my greeting or well wishes.

I thought maybe, being old, he was hard-of-hearing and couldn't afford a hearing aid. Maybe he could afford a hearing aid but his batteries were dead and he hadn't gone to the neighborhood drug store yet to buy fresh ones.

Maybe he just didn't understand much English. Maybe he thought teenagers, or those of my generation, weren't even worth talking or paying attention to! Or maybe I reminded him of someone he might have lost in the Holocaust and he did not want to be reminded of it.

One Saturday morning, right after Shabbat services, during Hanukkah, Nachum, as usual, was sitting at a table, by himself, in the congregation's social hall, nibbling on sponge cake and sipping tea. He always drank strong dark hot tea, in a strange way. The hot tea was in a tall, clear glass with a long metal spoon in it. Before Nachum leaned over to sip the tea he would pick up a sugar cube and bite off a very tiny piece. Then he would carefully lift the glass to his lips and loudly sip the tea from the edge. I had seen this "ritual" before. My father's mother, my Bubbe Leah, who came over from Poland, sipped her tea in exactly the same way. She explained sugar was very scarce in "the old country." She would never put an entire sugar cube in a single cup of tea. That would be very wasteful, since sugar was a luxury back when she was young. My Bubbe Leah showed me how to nibble off a very small piece of sugar from the cube and place it under my tongue, before each sip of tea, to make the sugar cube last longer. She also explained the tall metal spoon absorbed the heat from the hot glass, making the tea cool faster.

While observing Nachum doing the same tea "ritual," I walked up to his table (on the dare from my friends) and stopped. I looked down at him and said, "Good Shabbat." He put down his piece of sponge cake and glass of tea. Then he stared directly up at me. Did I offend him? Was he going to stand up and punch me in the nose? Instead he looked up at me and said, in his broken English, "Same to you, young man and a very Happy Hanukkah."

I froze in my tracks and looked around. "No, young man: Happy Hanukkah to you," Nachum said staring at me with his dark, steel-blue eyes. "Come here. Happy Hanukkah to you."

Pointing to an empty chair next to him he said, "Come, 'boychic.' Sit. Sit down, here, next to me for a few minutes."

I was stunned. I trembled as I obeyed his command and sat down in the chair next to him. I looked at my friends across the room for help. They ignored me by looking in the opposite direction. So much for my "friends."

Nachum continued to stare at me with those dark, steel-blue eyes. He smiled. It was the first time I noticed he had several gold teeth. He looked to his left. He looked to his right. Then he looked directly back at me. His face lit up. "Did you ever hear of the legend of Hanukkah Harry'?" he asked.

"No, sir," I said shaking my head. "I never heard of the legend of a 'Hanukkah Harry.'"

"Now, my little 'mensch', you will," Nachum said.

As I sat next to the old man he put his arm firmly around my shoulders. As he drew me closer to him, this is exactly what Nachum told me, word for word…

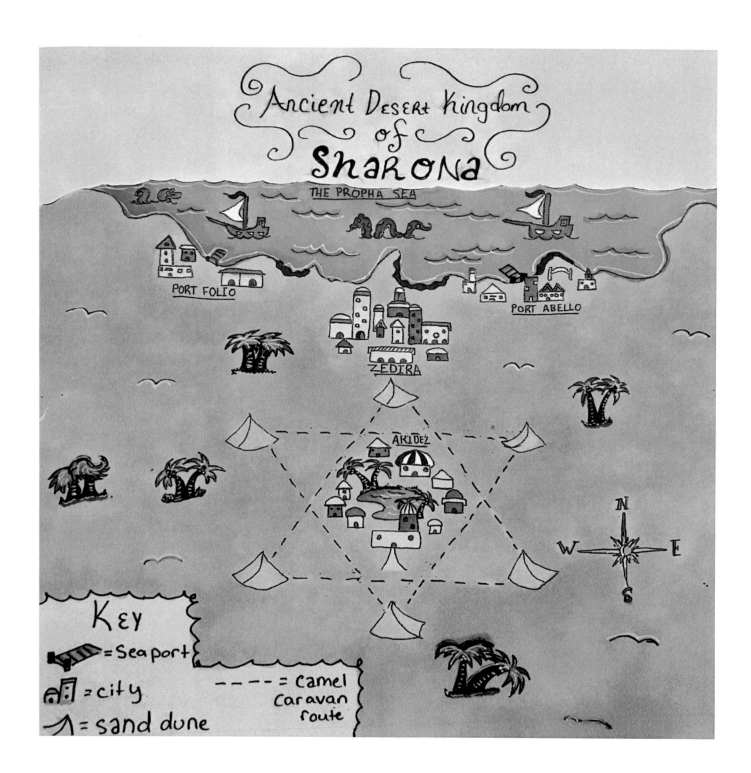

Chapter One

The legend of Hanukkah Harry began a very long time ago in a tiny desert oasis village called Aridez. Aridez was once part of the ancient desert kingdom of Sharona.

If you look at an ancient map of the region you will see Aridez was located near the southern shore of the Propha Sea. Between the two busy Propha Sea seaports of Port Folio and Port Abello, stood Sharona's capital city of Zedira. Directly south of Zedira stood six giant sand dunes that formed the shape of The Star of David. (There was How-ya Dune, How-shi Dune, How-zit Dune, How-dae Dune, How-mai Dune and How-zi Dune.)

In the exact center of the six sand dune formation was the desert oasis village of Aridez. Aridez was the only watering hole for camel caravans for many miles around.

Long before things were delivered by airplane, train, truck, or van, camels delivered everything from one place to another, especially in the ancient desert world.

Aridez was a typical ancient desert oasis village, complete with shops, restaurants and other buildings. Two places made Aridez very popular. One was the regional headquarters of Camel Herders' of Aridez, International (CHAI), Local #18. The camel herders' union building had a large hall that was used for weddings, receptions, and Bar Mitzvah and Bat Mitzvah parties. It was the main place for all of the area's large social gatherings.

The other popular place in Aridez was "Harry's Camel Lot." Harry the Camel Salesman was Aridez' most famous buyer and seller of camels in the entire ancient desert kingdom of Sharona, and even beyond! "Harry's Camel Lot" was located directly across the road from the from the camel herders' union hall.

Thanks to his Meerkat helpers, Morty and Manny watching his camels, Harry the Camel Salesman could be seen, daily, sitting at a large round wooden table in front of the camel herders' union hall. There he would be talking with many of the camel herders, most notably the three elected officers of the union. They would be sitting around the large table drinking their favorite beverage: Yisro Ale.

Harry's beautiful wife, Polly Esther, was an excellent seamstress and hat maker. Her handmade cloth outfits, especially her hats, were just as famous as Harry and his camels.

Polly Esther was so busy creating, designing, and sewing, especially her hats, that she hired another seamstress, Sue Coat, to help her plus a tailor, Ray Yahn. When they were all very busy, Polly Esther's mother, Ma Jongg, could be called upon to help them.

Polly Esther's hats were also famous because of the way she advertised and displayed them. She did not put her hats on fake heads to show in a store window. She showed off her famous hats by placing them on the heads of her husband's camels!

Whenever Polly Esther put a new hat on one of Harry's camels, the camel would parade around on the streets of Aridez to display her latest creation for sale.

Not only was Polly Esther known for her hats, but she was just as famous for her home made matzo ball soup! Whenever she boiled a pot of her matzo ball soup the aroma filled the streets of Aridez. One whiff of Polly Esther's boiling matzo ball soup made everyone in Aridez know Friday sundown and Shabbat were near.

Chapter Two

One day Harry the Camel Salesman was sitting at the large table in front of the camel herders' union hall, directly across the road from his Camel Lot. He was talking to Humphrey "Hump" Withers, president of the union, Horace "Hoc" Stifle, vice president, and Patterson "Pad" Pastern, secretary. As they all sipped their Yisro Ale, Hump, Hoc, and Pad told Harry about a very big problem they had.

"Our large hall is stuffed with toys," said Hump.

"There are so many toys crammed and jammed into the hall that we can't rent it out anymore for big social events," explained Hoc.

"The place is overflowing with toys from wall to wall and ceiling to floor," added Pad.

Harry put down his drink and thought for a moment.

"I don't understand," said Harry. "How did your large hall get filled with so many toys?"

Hump, Hoc, and Pad explained.

"We camel herders work hard during the day by leading camel caravans along the vast desert trade routes of Sharona from one oasis to another," said Hump.

"Our problem was during the night, when the camels were asleep," explained Hoc. "We didn't have anything to do. So we began to make toys from what we found left behind by other camel caravans. We used rope, parts of baskets, pieces of leather, dried palm tree leaves, coconut shells, and other things we found lying around in the desert sand."

"When our camel caravans returned to Aridez," explained Pad, "we put the toys we made in the union hall. At first the toys did not take up much space. Then, as time went on, the toys began piling up and taking up more and more space. Soon the parties and social events had less hall space to use."

Hump, Hoc, and Pad told Harry that the hall could not hold any more toys. They did not know what to do.

"Either we have to stop renting out the hall and go into the toy business," said Hump, "or get rid of all the toys and go back into renting out the hall again."

"Give me some time to think about your problem, my dear friends," said Harry.

Hump, Hoc, and Pad had to get ready to lead another camel caravan about to leave Aridez. They left Harry sitting alone at the table in front of the union hall drinking his Yisro Ale and thinking of an answer to the camel herders' toy and hall space problems.

Just then Harry looked up to see his lead camel, Shamash, walking in front of the union hall wearing one of Polly Esther's new hats. Shamash was being followed by a group of little boys and girls.

"Why are they following Shamash through the streets of Aridez?" Harry asked himself.

Harry stood up and walked over to one of the little boys he knew, named Amir Child, and asked, "Why are you and your friends following Shamash around the streets of Aridez?"

"Because," replied Amir, "we don't have anything else to do. We are not old enough to go to school. Besides that we don't have anything to play with."

"Hmmm," said Harry as Amir Child and his friends marched away, behind Shamash. "That's something to think about." As Harry was thinking he suddenly smelled his wife, Polly Esther's, famous matzo ball soup.

"It must be Friday," thought Harry. "Polly Esther always makes a big pot of boiling matzo ball soup every Shabbat."

Harry stood up from the table and followed the aroma of Polly Esther's famous matzo ball soup across the road to her kitchen.

Chapter Three

It happened so fast that no one saw it! Well, almost no one.

A meteor shot across the bright and sunny daylight desert sky directly over Aridez! As the meteor entered the Earth's atmosphere it made a long fireball trail in the sky.

Being daylight it went unnoticed by most everyone in Aridez. Everyone that is except Harry the Camel Salesman's two helpers: Morty Meerkat and his brother, Manny Meerkat.

Upon entering the Earth's atmosphere the meteor broke up into millions of tiny pieces. The particles rained down, like a tiny sand storm, over a very small area of Aridez. All the particles fell directly through Polly Esther's kitchen window and right into her pot of boiling matzo ball soup!

Chapter Four

Not too long after the sandy meteor shower stopped, Harry quietly tip-toed up to his wife, Polly Esther's kitchen window. He had not seen the meteor shower of hot dust fall into the soup. He looked directly down into the boiling pot. It smelled so good that Harry could not wait. He reached in through the window and picked up a large wooden spoon that was sitting on the edge of the stove. He dipped the spoon into the boiling pot of matzo ball soup. He carefully raised the spoonful of hot soup to his lips and blew on it to cool it off. Just as he was just about to take a sip he looked down and saw what looked like sand in the spoonful of soup.

Just then: "Harry! What are you doing?" shouted Polly Esther standing in her kitchen doorway.

SPLASH!

Harry dropped the spoon into the pot of boiling matzo ball soup.

"Now you've done it!" said Polly Esther, putting her hands on her hips. "By dropping the spoon in the boiling pot you have ruined my Shabbat matzo ball soup!"

Harry was ashamed of himself.

"Now I'll have to take this pot of soup outside to cool off before I throw it away and make another pot of matzo ball soup before sundown and Shabbat dinner," said Polly Esther as she grabbed two potholders and picked up the pot of soup by its two handles.

Harry stared down at the kitchen floor still ashamed of himself.

"I'm sorry," he said. "You know, dear, maybe it's a good idea to make another pot of matzo ball soup. It looked like someone poured sand in it."

Polly Esther shook her head at Harry. "It's always an excuse with you," she replied. "Now get away from my kitchen and go back to your camels."

Still ashamed, Harry helped Polly Esther carry the pot of soup outside to cool off. While Polly Esther went back to her sewing Harry went back to his camels.

As the pot of matzo ball soup sat cooling off, Harry did not see that all nine of his camels had gotten out of their corral. The gate had been left open! The camels had also smelled Polly Esther's pot of boiling matzo ball soup. They slowly trotted over from their open corral to the pot of cooling sandy matzo ball soup. The camels politely took turns drinking the soup from the pot until it was almost gone.

Looking over at his house from his camel lot, Harry suddenly saw his camels drinking from Polly Esther's soup pot.

"Hey! Get back to your corral!" shouted Harry. "Get out of here! Polly Esther is already mad at me and is going to be mad at you too!" he said as he led his camels back to their corral.

"I have to talk to my two helpers, Manny Meerkat and Morty Meerkat," said Harry, "about how those camels are getting out of the corral."

Chapter Five

Manny Meerkat and his brother Morty Meerkat worked for Harry and his camels all their lives.

Many years ago, while leading a very large caravan, the camel herders found two baby meerkats deserted in the desert. They wrapped them in a blanket and brought them back to Aridez. The camel herders gave the pair of orphaned baby meerkats to Harry and Polly Esther who raised them. Over the years Harry taught Manny and Morty how to care for and pamper his camels by washing, combing, exercising and feeding them. It was Manny and Morty's special care and treatment that made "Harry's Camel Lot" known throughout the ancient desert kingdom of Sharona, and even beyond!

Now Manny and Morty were having trouble with nine of Harry's camels. How did the camels get out of their corral? Who left the corral gate open? Manny and Morty noticed ever since the camels drank Polly Esther's sandy matzo ball soup they were acting very strange.

Chapter Six

While Manny Meerkat and Morty Meerkat were trying to figure out how the camels got out of their corral and began acting so strange, Harry went back to solving the camel herders' toy problem.

Harry thought if he went back to the camel herders' union hall table and sat in the same chair, the answer to the problem would eventually come to him sooner or later.

Just as Harry down sat down at the table in front of the camel herders' union hall, Shamash, his lead camel, once again paraded by the front of the union hall wearing another of Polly Esther's new hats. Amir Child and his little friends were still following Shamash.

Hmmm," thought Harry, "there is a hall overflowing with toys behind me and a whole bunch of little children without toys in front of me."

Harry suddenly got an idea!

He sat at the table until the camel herders returned to Aridez from leading their latest camel caravan.

Soon Hump, Hoc, and Pad arrived and sat down at the table with Harry. They looked very tired.

"How was this caravan?" asked Harry.

"It was hotter than usual, this trip, but it was okay," said Hump.

"We sure covered a lot of hot, dry, sandy desert," said Hoc.

"We've got enough sand in our boots," said Pad, "to add a seventh sand dune to the other six sand dunes that surround Aridez."

"So, what's new with you, Harry?" asked Hump.

Harry smiled at his friends.

"I think I solved your hall-full-of-toys problem," he replied smiling.

"You did?" said Hump, Hoc, and Pad together.

"Yes," said Harry, "I think I have."

"Well?" said Hump.

"It's really very simple when you think about it," explained Harry. "You have a hall full of toys. Right? Aridez, in fact a lot of Sharona and beyond, have children. Right?"

"So?" said Hoc.

"So," said Harry, "let's give the camel herders' hand-made toys to the children!"

"But how?" asked Pad.

Harry thought for a moment. "I just solved one part of your problem," he said. "Give me a little more time to solve the rest of it."

After a few minutes of silence, Hump jumped up out of his chair.

"Maybe we can help you with that part of the problem!" he said.

Suddenly Hoc jumped out of his chair. "I've got it!" he said to Harry. "We have the toys and you have the camels, while lots of Aridez and the rest of Sharona's children have no toys. Right? Then the answer is very simple, indeed!"

"What do you mean?" asked Harry.

Pad jumped out of his chair. "I think I know what Hump and Hoc are getting at!" he said.

Pad then explained. "We load up Harry's camels with our special, hand-made toys and deliver them to all the children!"

"Do you know how long that would take?" asked Harry. "You know very well, being camel herders, just how slow camels are."

Just then Manny Meerkat and Morty Meeekat ran up to Harry.

"The camels got loose again," said Morty.

"Then let's go round them up again," said Harry. He excused himself from Hump, Hoc, and Pad.

Chapter Seven

Harry, Manny, and Morty began looking for Harry's nine missing camels again!

They looked everywhere!

Morty suddenly got an idea. He led Harry and Manny back to Polly Esther's kitchen. Sure enough there were all nine of Harry's camels, drinking more of Polly Esther's sandy matzo ball soup!

"Hey!" shouted Harry at the camels. "Get out of here! Get back to your corral!"

The nine camels suddenly stopped drinking the soup, looked up at Harry, Manny, and Morty. They turned around and slowly walked back to their corral.

Then something very strange happened.

Harry was very mad because the camels were walking too slow, led by Shamash, his lead camel.

"Oy, Shamash!" Harry shouted at his lead camel.

Suddenly Shamash began to slowly lift off the ground and float up toward the sky!

While chasing after some of the other slow camels, Manny shouted out their names: "Oy, Lox! Oy, Bagel! Oy, Borsht! Oy, Dreidel!"

Suddenly the four camels began to slowly lift off the ground and float toward the sky too!

"Oy, Farfel! Oy, Knish! Oy, Latka! Oy, Yenta!" shouted Morty. The same thing happened: those four camels slowly lifted off the ground, and they, too, floated up toward the sky!

Harry, Manny, and Morty ran after the nine flying camels and followed them back to "Harry's Camel Lot" corral. All nine camels then gently floated back down to the ground.

Harry, Manny, and Morty then stood outside the camels' corral to try and figure out what they just saw.

"I just don't understand," said Harry. "Those camels started acting very strange just after they drank Polly Esther's matzo ball soup the first time."

"Sandy soup," added Manny.

"Why was the soup so gritty and sandy?" asked Morty.

"Remember," said Manny, "that the camels drank the soup after we just happened to look up and see that meteor entering the Earth's atmosphere.? Then we saw the meteor shower of fine, hot sand all fall directly into the pot of Polly Esther's boiling matzo ball soup."

"Do you think the sand from the meteor shower that fell into the soup made the camels fly?" asked Morty.

"Hmmm," said Harry. "If that's true then I just got another idea to help my friends, the camel herders!"

Harry turned to Morty and Manny and said, "Stay here and watch those camels. Make sure the gate to their corral is closed tight. I'll be right back."

Harry returned to the camel herders' union hall. Hump, Hoc, and Pad were still sitting at the big table.

"Did you find all your nine camels?" asked Hump.

"Oh, yeah!" said Harry. He then smiled and said, "I just figured out how we can deliver all your special hand-made toys to the children of Aridez, Zedira, the ancient desert kingdom of Sharona, and even beyond!"

"How?" asked Hoc.

"Listen very carefully to what I am about to tell you," said Harry. "Tomorrow night is the very first night of Hanukkah. After lighting the first candle in the menorah and eating dinner with your families, meet me and the other camel herders back here at your union hall."

"But why?" asked Hoc.

"What for?" asked Pad

"Show up and you will see," said Harry with a big smiled that covered his face from ear to ear.

Chapter Eight

Just as planned, on the very first night of Hanukkah, Harry, Manny, Morty, and all the camel herders lit their first menorah candle and ate with their families. They then excused themselves and met at the back of their union hall.

When the camel herders arrived they saw Harry's nine camels standing in a single-file line. Each camel had a basket of woven dried palm tree leaves on both sides of their humps. In front of the line of Harry's nine camels stood Manny Meerkat and Morty Meerkat.

"What is going on here?" asked Hump.

"You'll see," said Harry. He told all the camel herders to form a line from the back of the union hall to the line of Harry's nine camels.

Soon all nine camels were loaded with overflowing baskets of the camel herders' hand-made toys.

"Now what?" asked Hoc.

"You'll see," said Harry.

"See what?" asked Pad.

"Just stand back and watch," said Harry.

Harry got on to the back of his last camel in line, Yenta. He turned to the camel herders and said, "Watch this, but, whatever you do, please DO NOT tell your wives and families what you are about to see. Meet me back here tomorrow night at the same time so we can load up the camels again to deliver more toys."

Then as Harry shouted "Oy!" before each of his nine camels' names, the camels slowly lifted off the ground, floated up toward the sky, and flew out of sight into the dark desert, nighttime sky.

Hump, Hoc, Pad, and the rest of the camel herders looked up toward the night sky but could not believe what they saw.

"Amazing!" said Hump.

"Unbelievable!" said Hoc.

"Our wives and family are not going to believe what we just saw!" said Pad.

"Remember what Harry told us," said Hump. "Not a word to anyone!"

As the camel herders returned to their homes and families that first night of Hanukkah they still could not believe what they saw. They kept their promise to Harry and did not tell their wives or children what they saw that very first night of Hanukkah.

Chapter Nine

For the next six nights, after Hanukkah candles were lit and Hanukkah family dinners were over, the camel herders, plus Harry, Manny, and Morty, all met back at the union hall to load as many toys onto Harry's nine camels as they could.

Again the camel herders stood in disbelief as Harry climbed on his last camel in line, Yenta. Again Harry said "Oy!" and called out each one of his camels' names as they lifted slowly off the ground and floated up into Aridez' dark, desert night time sky.

Chapter Ten

The eighth and final day of Hanukkah found Harry, Manny, Morty sitting with Hump, Hoc, and Pad at the large table in front of the camel herders' union hall once again.

"Our wives and families have been wondering what's been going on the last seven nights," said Hump.

"Yeah," said Hoc. "They want to know where we've been going and what we've been doing after we light the Hanukkah candles and eat dinner.

"By the time we load all our hand-made toys onto the camels and get back home," said Pad, "everyone is already asleep!"

Harry thought for a moment.

"I just looked inside the union hall," he said. "All the toys are almost gone. I think we can completely empty out the hall of the rest of the toys and finish up tonight!"

"So?" said Hump.

"So," said Harry, "light the last and eighth and final Hanukkah candle on the menorah tonight and eat your Hanukkah dinner. Then bring your wives and children *with you* to the back of the union hall so everyone can finally see what we have been doing the last seven nights."

"After all," said Hoc, "it's the eighth and last night of Hanukkah."

"What better way," said Pad, "to celebrate the last night of Hanukkah then to be together with family and friends."

"We can do something very special tonight," said Manny.

"We can do this wonderful thing all together," said Morty.

And that's exactly what happened.

Chapter Eleven

Harry, Manny, Morty, Polly Esther, Sue Coat, Ma Jongg, and Ray Yahn, along with all of Aridez' camel herders and their families waited until sundown on the eighth and final night of Hanukkah. After lighting the eighth and final Hanukkah candle on their menorahs and eating dinner, they all met at the back of the camel herders' union hall.

Everyone watched as the camel herders helped Harry, Manny, and Morty line up the nine camels and fill their baskets with the last of the camel herders' special hand-made toys.

Just as Harry was about to say "goodbye" to his wife before getting on his last camel in line, Yenta, Polly Esther walked up to her husband.

"Harry, I watched you, Manny and Morty put the baskets that Sue Coat, Ma Jongg, and I made on the camels. I know what you are doing is very special. So I made something very special just for you."

Polly Esther then presented Harry with a dark blue velvet coat with matching pants and yarmulke.

"What is this?" asked Harry.

"What if the children see just plain old Harry the Camel Salesman from Aridez delivering toys?" asked Polly Esther.

"The children are not going to see me. They are supposed to be sleeping," said Harry.

"But what if they all *aren't* sleeping? I don't want those children to see just plain old Harry the Camel Salesman, from Aridez, giving them special, hand-made toys," Polly

Esther said. "You are doing something very special so you should wear something very special like this suit and yarmulke I made just for you on this eighth and final night of Hanukkah."

Harry bent over to give Polly Esther a kiss.

Just then, Pad ran up to Harry.

"Wait, Harry!' shouted Pad. "I just got an idea! Wait right here. Don't move. I'll be right back." Pad turned around and ran into the union hall. He immediately returned with a pair of shiny black leather boots.

"Someone left this pair of boots in the union hall after a party a long time ago and never came back for them," explained Pad.

Pad handed the boots to Harry.

"What are these boots for, Pad?" asked Harry.

"Harry, we give presents to each other on Hanukkah," said Pad. "Besides I think you need these boots to keep your feet warm."

"This is from me to you," said Pad. "These are for **Hanukkah, Harry**."

"That's it!" shouted Polly Esther. "You are no longer Harry the Camel Salesman from Aridez. You are what Pad just said: You are now, '*Hanukkah Harry*.'"

Suddenly everyone let out a loud cheer. "YAY!"

Harry put on the blue velvet coat with eight gold buttons down the front of it, the blue velvet pants, and the matching blue velvet yarmulke (skull cap) that Polly Esther made, plus the black boots Pad gave him.

Harry the Camel Salesman from Aridez, was now **Hanukkah Harry**!

Then **Hanukkah Harry** got on Yenta, the last camel in line. He turned his head around toward the large crowd and smiled.

"Thank you, everyone!" he shouted to them.

"You better get going, *Hanukkah Harry*!" said Morty Meerkat.

"It's getting late already!" said Manny Meerkat.

As **Hanukkah Harry** shouted, "Oy!" and said each of the nine camels' names, they slowly lifted off the ground and floated up into the dark Aridez desert night sky to deliver toys to all the children of the ancient desert kingdom of Sharona and beyond!

"Oy, Shamash!"

"Oy, Lox!"

"Oy, Bagel!"

"Oy, Borsht!"

"Oy, Dreidel!"

"Oy, Farfel!

"Oy, Latka!"

"Oy, Knish!"

"Oy, Yenta!"

As everyone looked up toward the dark desert night time sky above, they could just barely hear **Hanukkah Harry** shouting, "Oy! Oy! Oy! I'm giving each child a toy!!!"

And so began the Legend of **Hanukkah Harry**.

Chapter Twelve

Everyone headed back home on the eighth and final night of Hanukkah. Manny Meerkat and and his brother Morty Meerkat walked back toward Harry's Camel Lot to wait for Harry and the nine camels to return.

Morty turned to Manny. "I saw you pour something into the camels' drinking water just before we took them over to the camel herders' union hall that first night of Hanukkah," he said. "Were they drinking some of Polly Esther's leftover gritty, sandy matzo ball soup that made them fly that first time we saw them?"

"Yes," said Manny. "When we first saw the camels fly right after they drank Polly Esther's soup and we chased them back to their corral, I went back to the pot and poured all the left over soup into a little bottle. On each night of Hanukkah, before we led the camels to the union hall, I poured some of the gritty, sandy matzo ball soup into their drinking water to make them fly."

"I saw that little bottle, "said Morty. "There was only just barely enough left in that tiny bottle to last only one night. But miraculously, it lasted eight nights!"

Manny smiled and said, "It's a miracle. Isn't it?"

"You know, Manny," said Morty, "that story sounds very familiar, especially this time of year at Hanukkah."

After a moment of thought, Morty said, "Oh, I get it!"

Manny and Morty both smiled at each other and laughed out loud!

91957006R00027

Made in the USA
San Bernardino, CA
27 October 2018